This book
belongs to:

··

Typeset by Fuzzy Flamingo
www.fuzzyflamingo.co.uk

A catalogue for this book is available from the British Library.

For Donna

The moon looked down from up above, through a clear and cloudless sky.

He said, "Mother Earth, whatever is wrong, tell me why do you cry?"

You are beautiful, bountiful, the place where all life began.

That's the reason you were chosen to be the home of Man.

You of all the planets should be happy not upset.

Please stop crying, Mother Earth, you're getting everything wet."

"Oh Moon," said Mother Earth, "I weep for what Man is doing.

If people don't change their ways, the world will end in ruin.

Come closer, Moon, and take a look at how much of my forests they clear.

It seems to matter not, that millions of creatures live here.

Indigenous people suffer, as their land and homes are destroyed.

The traditions they hold so dear can no longer be enjoyed."

"Smog became a real menace as bigger their cities grew.

Now I choke on the fumes from their vehicles and the toxins their factories spew.

They poison my land with their rubbish, even though they make themselves ill.

They fill my oceans with plastic, and oil from their ships they spill.

They damage my wonderful coral reefs and the sea life that once prospered there.

They spoil my beautiful beaches, I really do despair."

"Man's actions do so much harm, but still they don't heed the warning.

As sea levels rise and rise because of global warming.

Polar bears will be in decline if they cannot hunt their prey.

When pack ice breaks into smaller pieces and simply melts away.

We need to get the message across, we have to try somehow.

For climate change is a very real threat; the time to act is now!"

"Mother Earth," said Moon, "of course, you are quite right.

I sympathise with your worrisome plight.

But perhaps you are fretting more than you should.

I'm sure most people are helpful and good."

"Well, thank you Moon," said Mother Earth, "for trying to bring me some cheer.

But let me tell you more, my friend, of some of the things I fear."

"Mankind is not so kind, it seems, indeed some people are bad.

They fight and hurt each other for things they wish they had.

They squabble over diamonds, minerals, oil and gold.

They think everything has a price; it can all be bought and sold.

Some people want to grab land, and take it by using force.

Displacing millions of people, as just a matter of course."

"Sometimes I feel so tired, Moon, and have nothing left to give.

I already provide enough for all mankind to live.

I have water and food in abundance, enough for everyone.

Yet half the world have too much, while the other half have none.

Rich men plunder my oceans and land, and do not seem to care.

Poor men struggle to survive, now tell me, Moon, is that fair?"

"I see," replied Moon quite solemnly, "no wonder you feel distressed.

Let me consult with the sun and see what she suggests.

She sees so much more than us; she is very old and wise.

So stop those tears right away and dry your puffy eyes."

Moon beckoned Sun to join them, she was happy to oblige.

Then she smiled her brightest smile and started to advise.

Sun said, "I'm inclined to agree with Moon's rosier projection.

More young people than ever before know the world needs their protection.

They see for themselves the harm humans cause,

And demand more action and environment laws.

Your problems are not too big to surmount;

And they will hold the world's leaders to account."

"They know they have issues they need to address,

Like recycling more and wasting less.

They want to reduce harmful gasses too.

Mother Earth, they want to take care of you.

They are learning about conservation and enhancing nature's forces.

And the need to swap fossil fuels for renewable energy sources."

"The next generation of leaders know more and understand,

That the future of the world lies in their own hands.

It may take a little while longer, and you might not escape unscathed.

But rest assured, Mother Earth, the world can still be saved."

Moon nodded in agreement and thanked the sun for her wisdom.

He said, "Sun you are the brightest star in our solar system."

Then Moon spoke to Mother Earth, "See… it's not too late.

As long as people act right away and don't just leave things to fate."

"Oh, Moon, I feel much better now," said Mother Earth with a smile.

"I feel much more optimistic than I have in quite a while."

She thanked the sun and the moon, and bid them both goodbye.

Then Moon, Sun and Mother Earth headed back to their own piece of the sky.

The three of them pondered for a while, reflecting on their discussion.

They were quietly confident Mother Earth wasn't bound for destruction.

Sun and Moon were convinced that young people could put the world right.

They had reassured their friend, the future could still be bright.

Mother Earth is feeling much better now, even though there is still much to do.

Because, where there's a will there's a way, so she is putting her trust in…

Coral Reef:

Coral reefs look like rocks, but they are actually tiny little animals called polyps. Polyps live on the outside of the reef and when they die, they form another layer of reef for new polyps to grow on. That's how the reef gets bigger. Reefs are found in shallow warm and clear water.

Indigenous People:

Indigenous people means the very first people who lived in any region, not those people that came later. They are often called aborigines, native people, first people and first nations. The United Nations prefers to use the term indigenous people because the other terms have often been used negatively in the past. Very often, indigenous people were made slaves by the new people who came to their land later. They were very badly treated and the new settlers robbed them and their land, and even killed many of them.

Solar System:

Our solar system consists of eight planets and their moons, which all orbit around our home star, the Sun. There are also asteroids and comets and other things orbiting it. The Sun is only one of more than 200 billion stars in the Milky Way.

Useful Organisations

www.planetsforkids.org

climatekids.nasa.gov

www.nwf.org

www.greenpeace.org

www.worldwildlife.org

www.foei.org

kids.nationalgeographic.com

www.oceanconnectors.org/kids/

www.ducksters.com

www.woodlandtrust.org.uk/

Printed in Great Britain
by Amazon

28972405R00021